A

for Sam

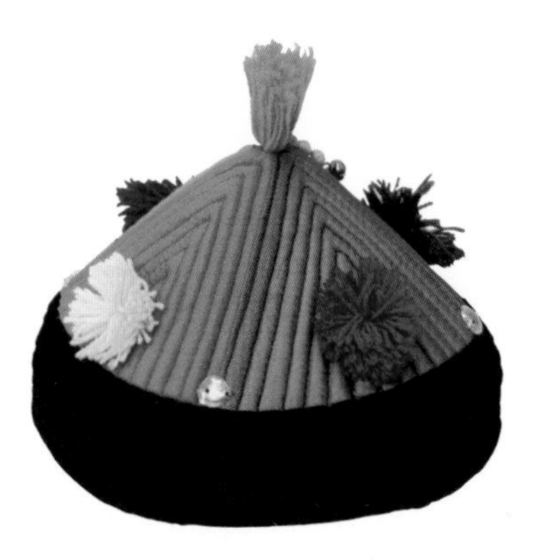

by Paul Wilson

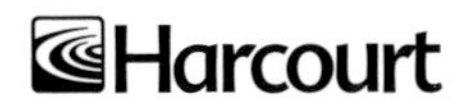

Orlando Boston Dallas Chicago San Diego

Visit *The Learning Site!*

www.harcourtschool.com

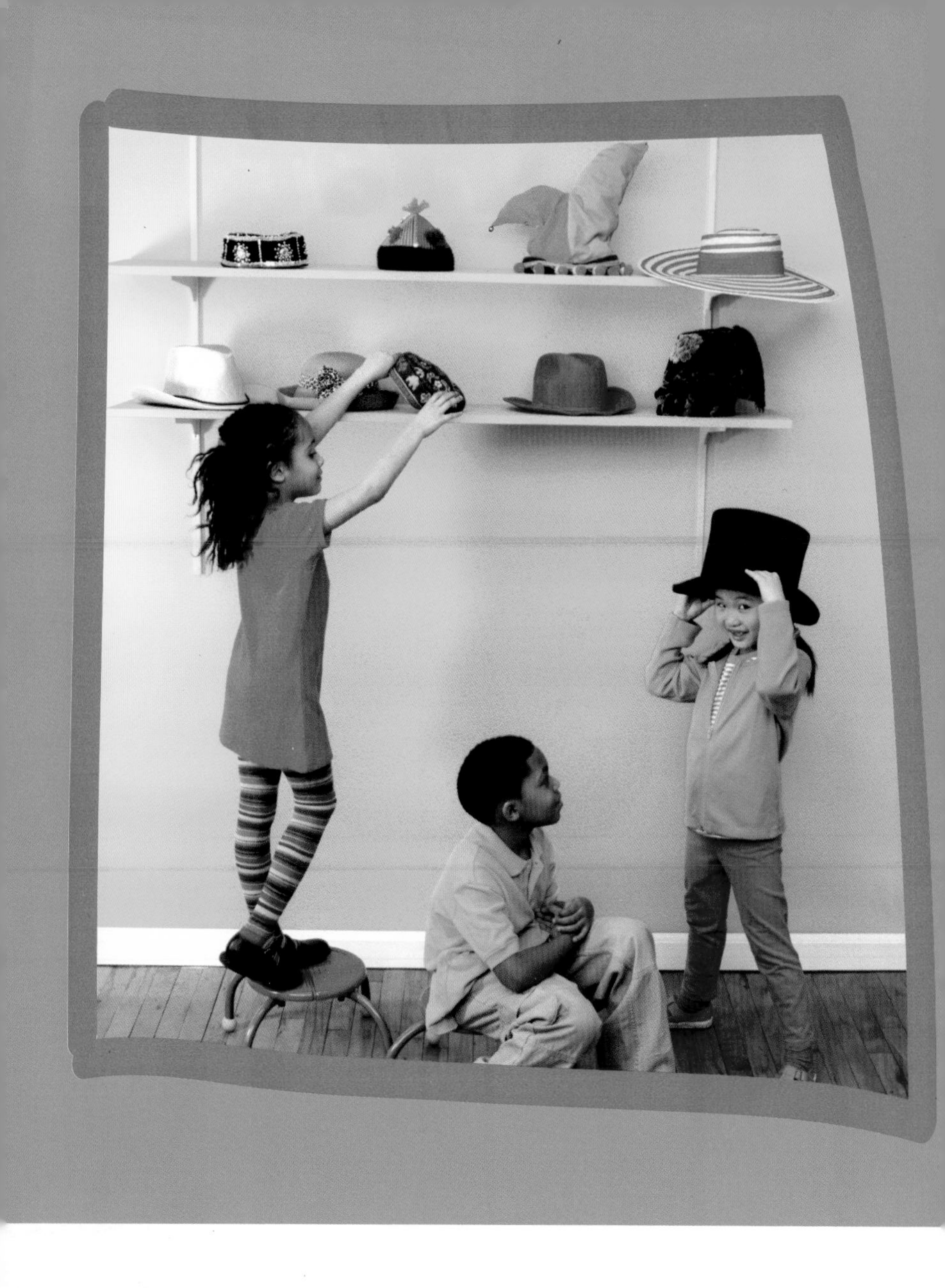

You got a hat down.

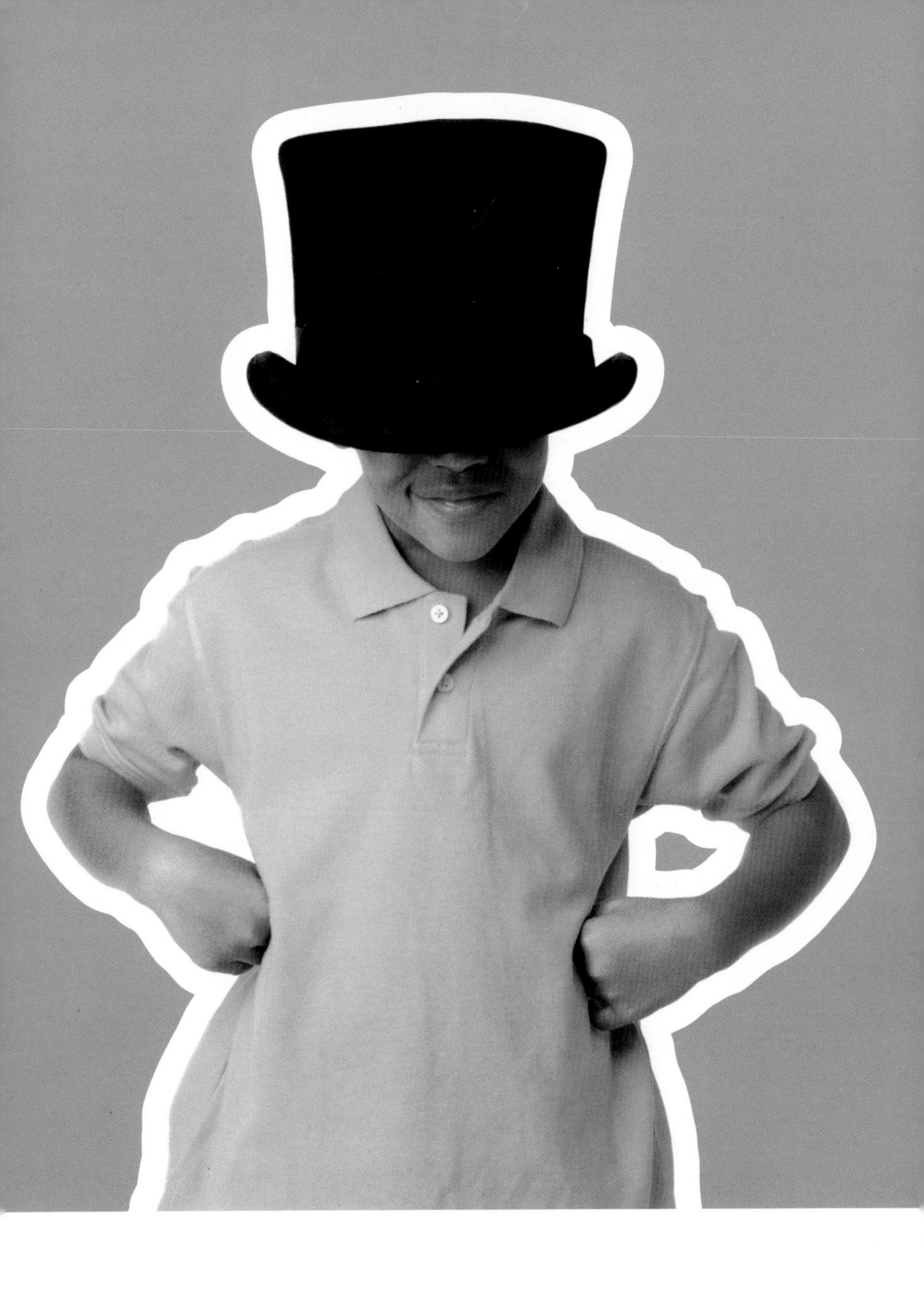

Can I have a hat?

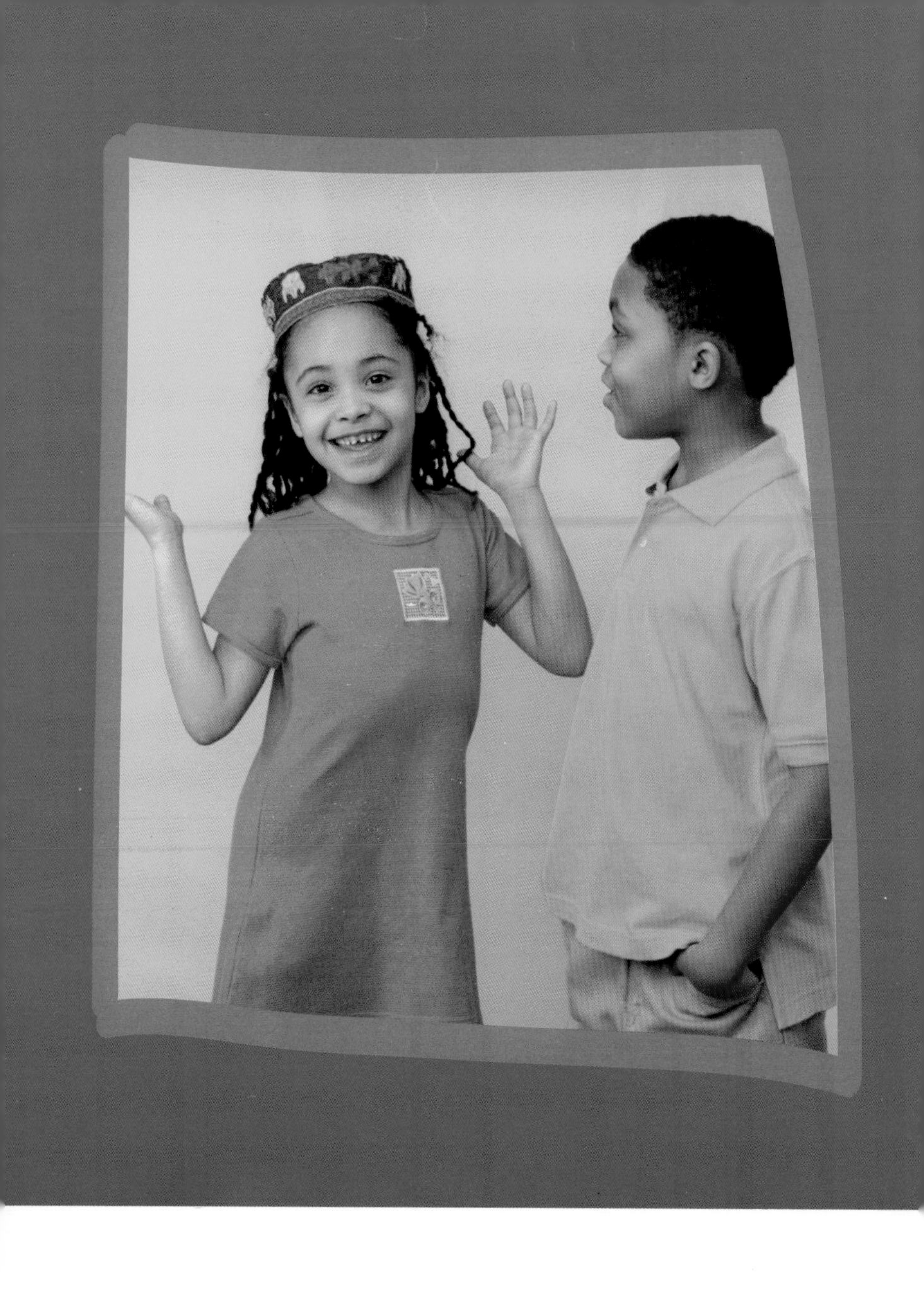

You got a hat down.

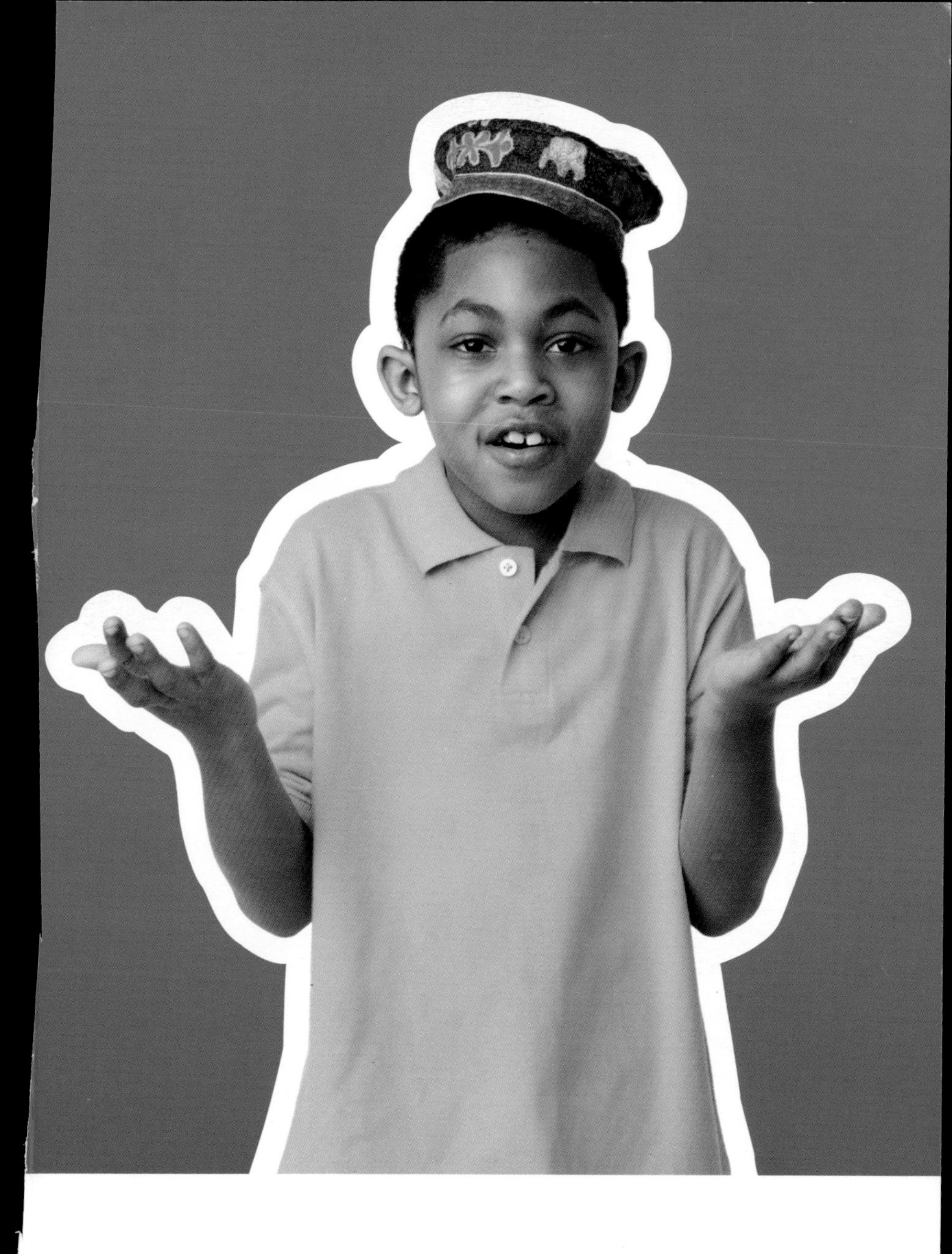

Can I have a hat?

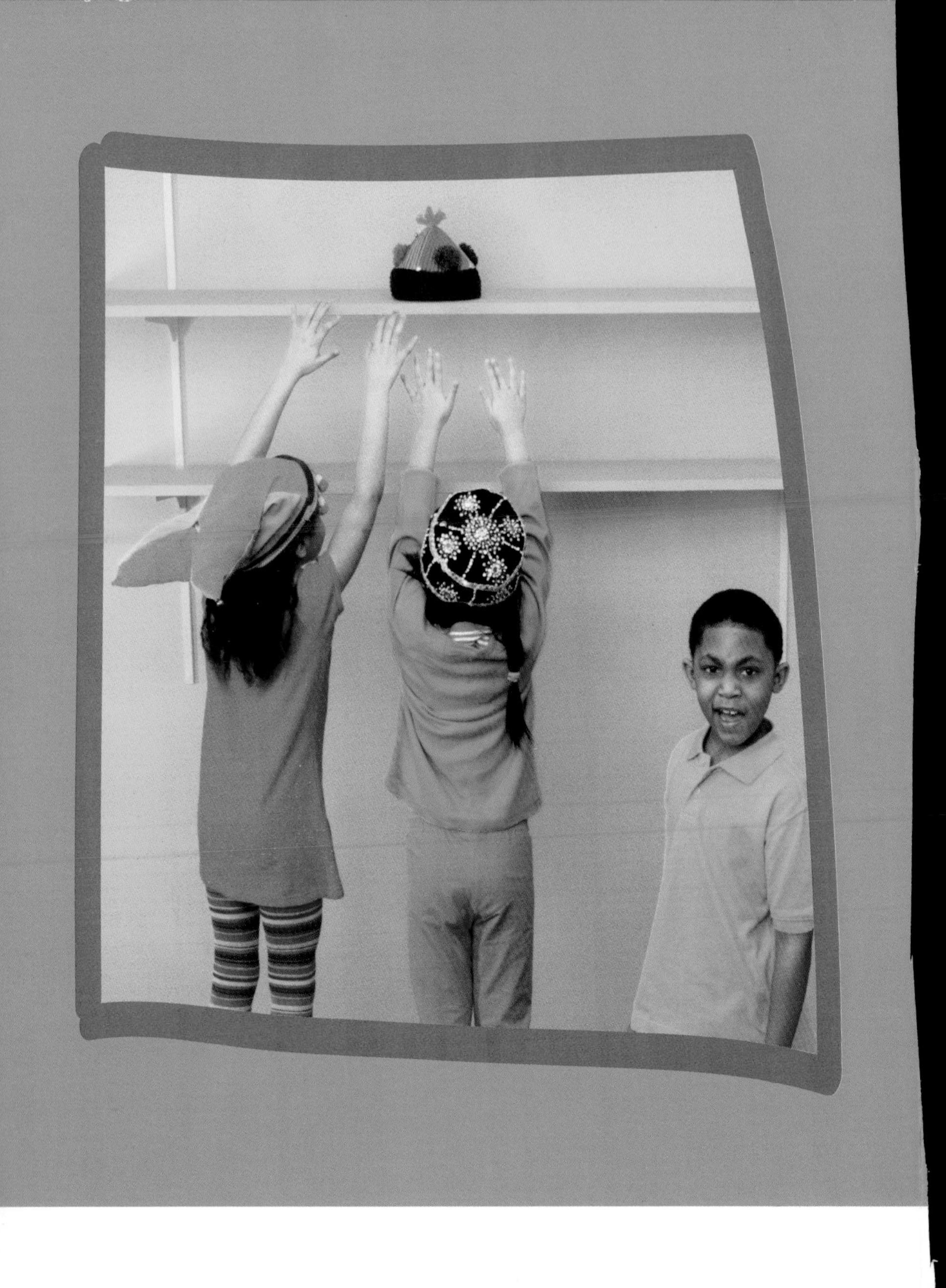

I see a hat up here.

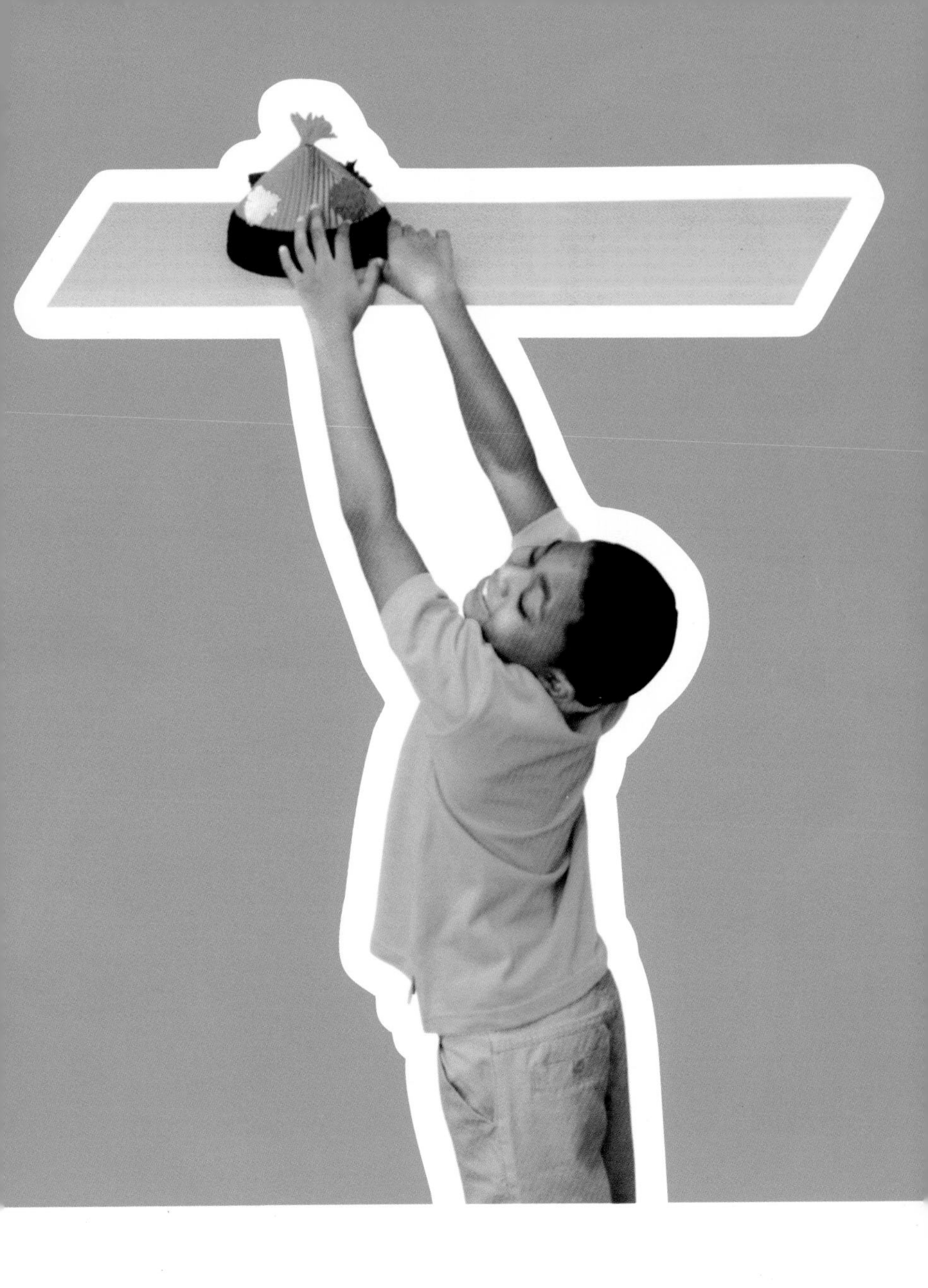

Can I go up?

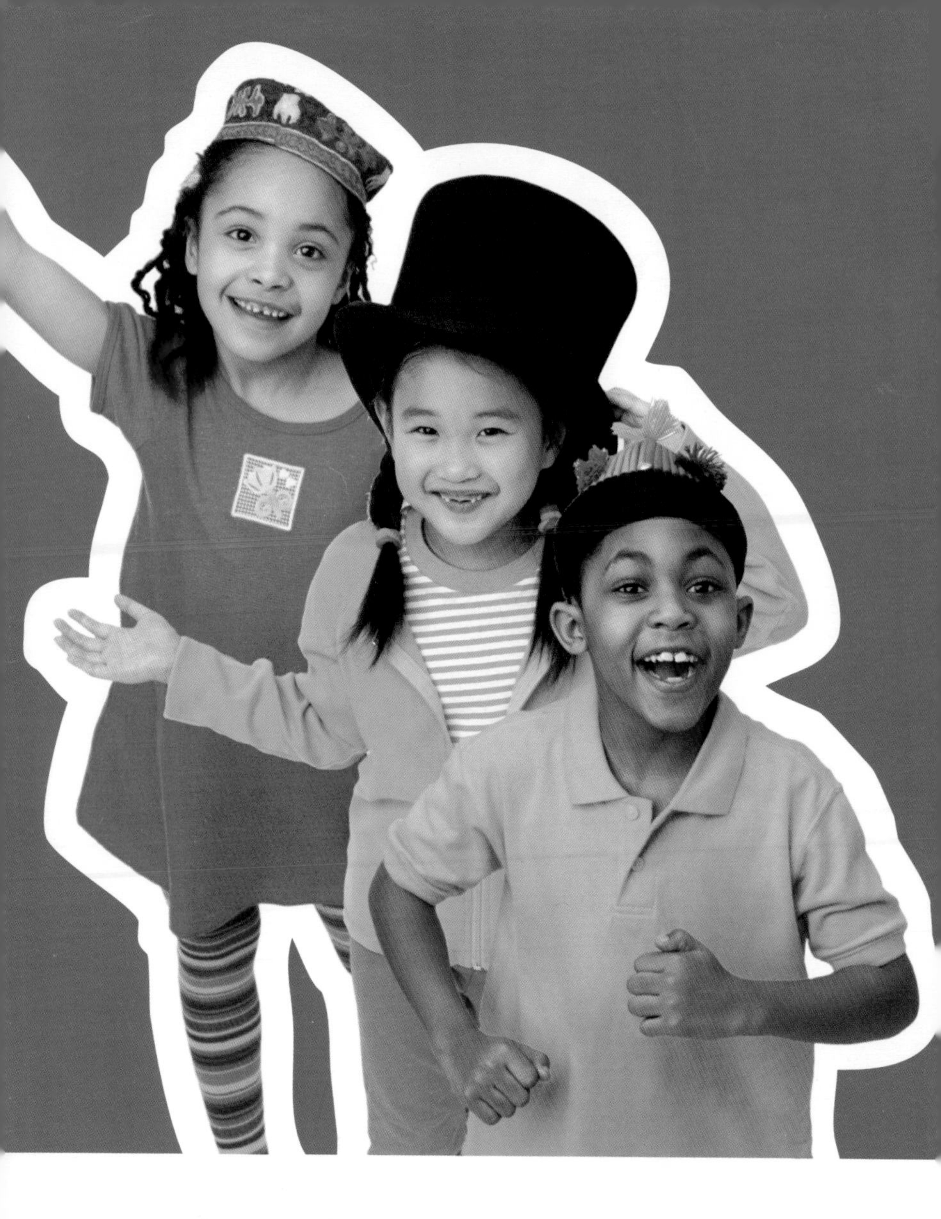

Look at the hat
for me!